P9-AQD-469

C0-AKF-422

STICKER MATH FUN

FOR 6-7 YEAR OLDS

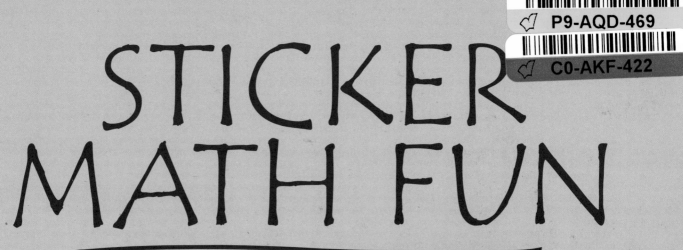

Fiona Watt

Designed and illustrated by Rachel Wells

Math consultant: Alice Cooper

Managing designer: Mary Cartwright Series editor: Jenny Tyler

American editor : Carrie Seay

Making 10

Which number do you need to add to each bee to make 10?
Find the flower sticker with the answer and put it on the stalk
beside the bee.

Rabbits' ears

Add the numbers on each rabbit's ears, then give it a carrot sticker with the answer on it.

Jumping frogs

Each frog is jumping from one lily pad to another. Add the numbers on the two lily pads, then put the water lily sticker with the answer on it beside them.

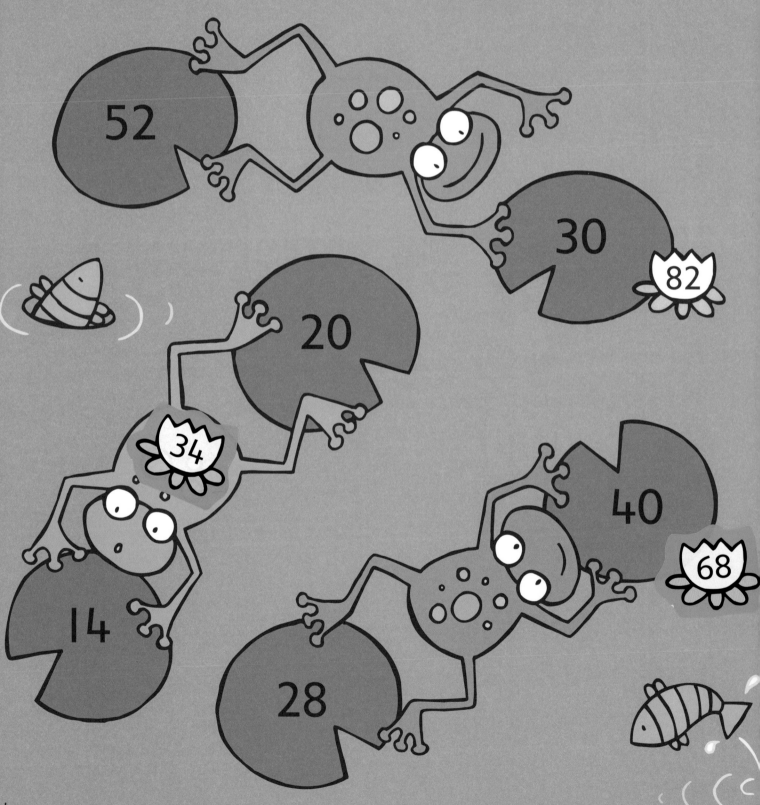

4

Waiting for a bus

Which number has been added to the first number in the line to make the second number? Add the same number each time for all the other animals, using a matching sticker.

Hungry caterpillars

These caterpillars have eaten holes in their leaves and now some of the numbers are missing. Do each sum, then find the correct shape of number sticker to fill in the hole.

$$5\;2$$
$$+\,2\,4$$
$$\overline{7\,6}$$

$$4\,5$$
$$+\,3\,4$$
$$\overline{7\,9}$$

$$1\;3$$
$$+\,2\,3$$
$$\overline{3\,6}$$

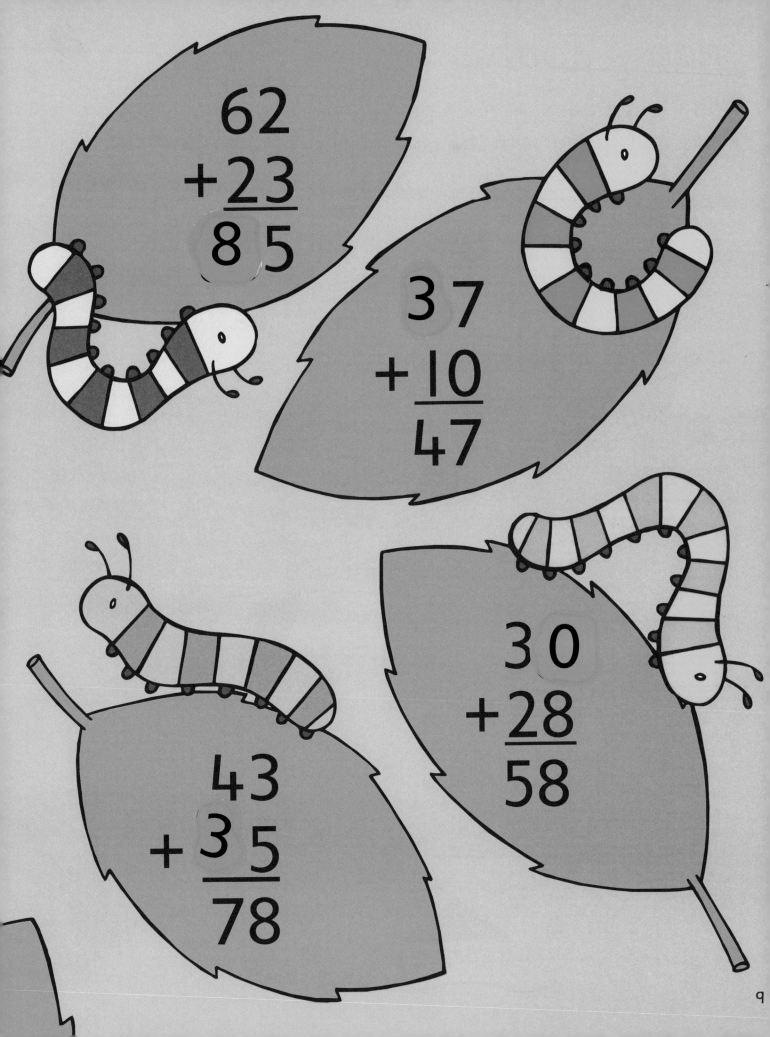

$$62 + 23 = 85$$

$$37 + 10 = 47$$

$$43 + 35 = 78$$

$$30 + 28 = 58$$

Seeing double

Add the numbers on each pair of twins.
Put a ball sticker with the correct answer next to them.

11

Magic squares

Find the correct number sticker to go in each empty square, so that the numbers in each row, column and diagonal add up to the same number.

Find the eggs

Use egg stickers to finish these sums.
Put a sticker of a bee next to the biggest total.

```
  2 2
+ 1 5
─────
  3 7
```

```
  1 4
+ 3 2
─────
  4 6
```

```
  4 2
+ 1 7
─────
  5 9
```

```
  6 6
+ 3 3
─────
  9 9
```

Juggling monkeys

Each monkey is standing on a box. The numbers on the juggling pins should add up to the number in the box. Find the missing pin stickers and put them above the monkey.

Score 100

Put dart stickers onto the dartboard to show
which two numbers add up to 100.

80   16

25   20

34   42

18   30

20   15

73   60

10   32

62   30

22

76

58   80

25   19

30   22

90   50

75   86

Find the flowers

Put flower stickers onto the stalks so that the numbers on the flowers add up to the number on the vase.

Build a wall

Add the numbers on two bricks which are next to each other. Put the correct brick sticker on the empty brick space directly above them. Keep doing this until you reach the top of the wall.

Number patterns

Write in the empty boxes so that each sum equals the number in the window at the top of the house.
Find two door numbers which add up to 26. Put a sticker of a package by the doors.

54

50 + 4
40 + 14
30 + 24
☐ + 34
☐ + 44
☐ + 54

79

☐ + 9
☐ + 19
☐ + 29
☐ + 39
☐ + 49
☐ + 59
☐ + 69

64

☐ + 4
☐ + 14
☐ + 24
☐ + 34
☐ + 44
☐ + 54

9

11

13

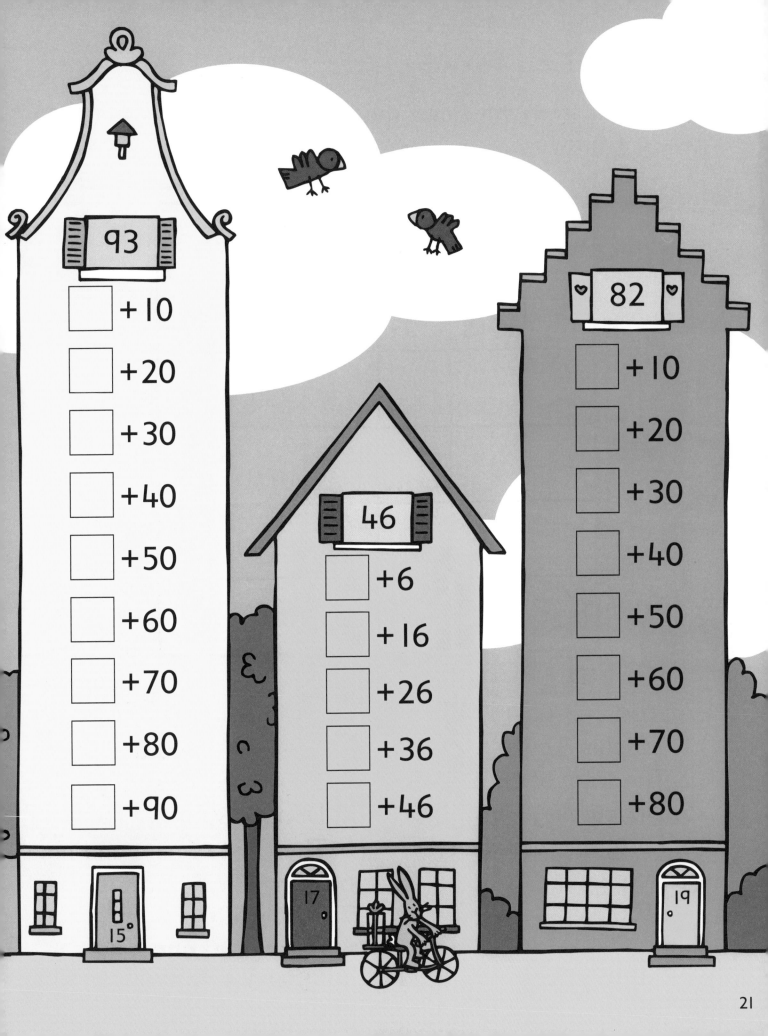

93

☐ +10
☐ +20
☐ +30
☐ +40
☐ +50
☐ +60
☐ +70
☐ +80
☐ +90

46

☐ +6
☐ +16
☐ +26
☐ +36
☐ +46

82

☐ +10
☐ +20
☐ +30
☐ +40
☐ +50
☐ +60
☐ +70
☐ +80

Number crosswords

Do the sums from the clues, then write the answers onto the crossword.

Across

1. 30 plus 32
2. The total of 20 and 18
5. Double fifty
6. Forty and eighteen
9. 50 plus 11
11. 100 + 1

Down

1. The sum of 60 and 6
3. Twenty plus twenty
4. Double 30
5. The total of nine and nine
6. 40 + 12
7. 50 plus 26
8. 40 and 40 altogether
10. 5 + 5 + 5

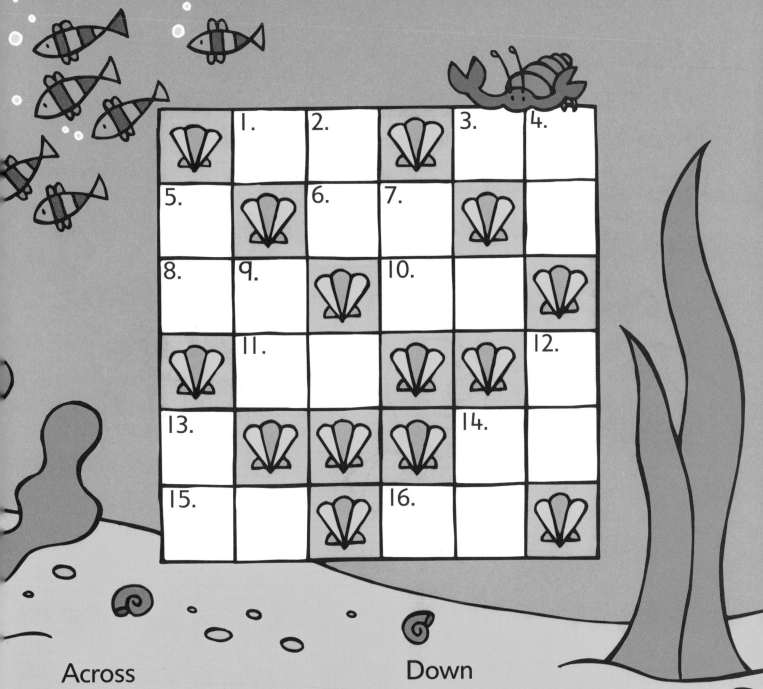

Across

1. Forty plus forty-four
3. 50 + 25
6. Sixty plus three
8. 52 and 4
10. Seven plus 20
11. One more than eighty
14. Fifty and six
15. 80 + 10
16. 82 plus 6

Down

2. 40 plus 6
4. Double twenty-five
5. 30 and 15
7. 30 + 1 + 1
9. 2 more than 66
12. Double thirteen
13. 36 + 3
14. Fifty plus eight

Which hat?

Each snowman is holding a board.
Do the sum on it then find the hat sticker with
the answer and put it on the snowman.

22 + 17

91 + 7

3 + 24

52 + 40

33 + 7

For most pages, there are some extra stickers which are not answers to the sums.

page 2

page 4-5

page 3

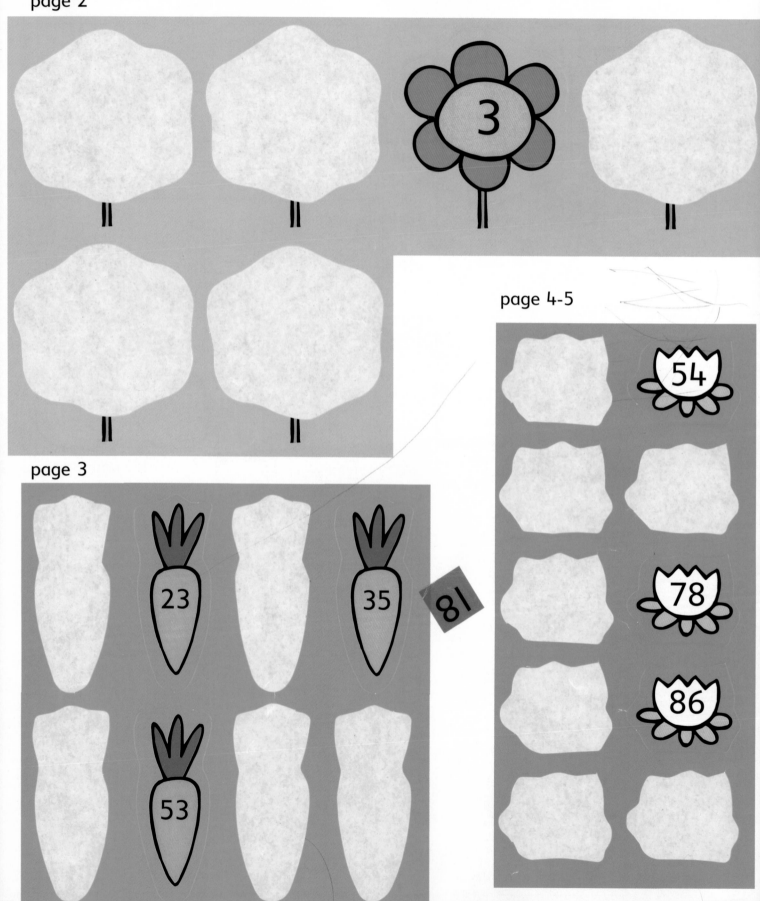

page 6-7

21

5 10 16

50

12 30 40

8 10 15 28

14 15 16 50

page 8-9

2 2 5

2 5 6 7

page 10-11

12 50 80

page 12

1 1 2 2 3 3 3 4

4 5 6 6 7 7 7

7 7 8 8 9 9 9

page 13

8

page 14-15

page 16

page 17

There are more flower stickers on the next page.

page 17

(15) (15) (20) (20) (25) (25)

page 18-19

3	3	4	4	5	5	
6	6	7	7	8	8	
8	9	9	11	11	11	
12	13		14	15	16	17
18	20	22	22	23	24	25

| | 26 | 38 | 46 |

page 20-21

page 24

27   34   89   40   88

28   92   98   36   39

Subtracting

Jumping back

Look at the sum at the end of each row of stepping stones. Put your finger on the stone with the first number in the sum, then count back along the stones to take away the second number. Put a frog sticker on the stone you land on.

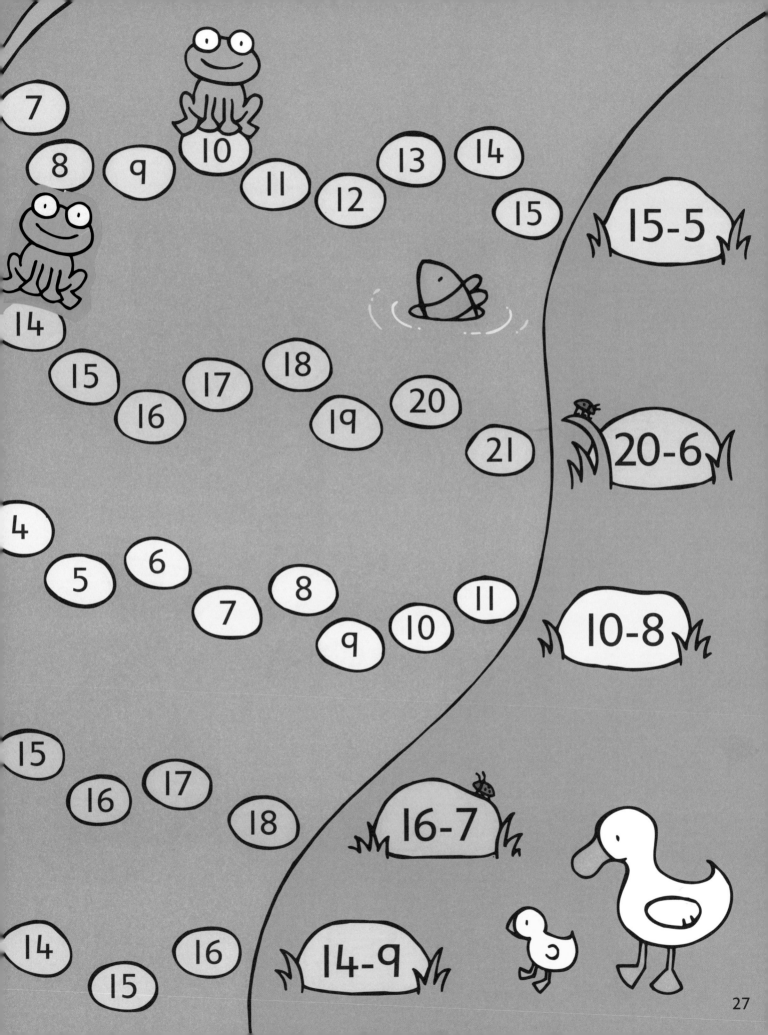

7

8　9　10　11　12　13　14

15

15-5

14

15　17　18

16　19　20

21

20-6

4

5　6　8　11

7　9　10

10-8

15

16　17

18

16-7

14　16

15

14-9

Blowing bubbles

Take away the number on the fish from the number in the bubble next to its mouth. Put a bubble sticker with the answer in the next bubble. Take away the number on the fish again from your answer and so on.

Knitting kittens

Do the sum on the kitten's knitting. Then, find the ball of yarn sticker with the answer and put it on the end of the kitten's yarn.

$$18 - 8$$

$$28 - 6$$

$$58 - 3$$

10

34
-2

66
-6

97
-5

49
-6

What's the difference?

What's the difference between the numbers that the owls are holding? Put a sticker with the answer beside the owl at the side of the page. Do the same for the other pairs of animals.

What's missing?

These worms have eaten holes in the apples and now some of the numbers are missing. Do each sum then find the correct shape of number sticker to fill the hole.

$$5\square$$
$$-\ 14$$
$$\overline{42}$$

$$55$$
$$-\ 3\square$$
$$\overline{23}$$

$$7\square$$
$$-\ 23$$
$$\overline{56}$$

$$62 - 31 = 31$$

$$9\square - 28 = 70$$

$$47 - \square5 = 22$$

Give me a number

Take away the number on the animal's T-shirt from the number in its hand. Then, find the answer sticker and put it in the other hand.

Take away dot to dot

Starting at 70, take away 2 and draw a line to the answer.
Then, take away 3 from that number and draw a line.
Continue taking away 2, then 3 in turn, to finish the picture.
Be careful, as there are some extra numbers you don't need.

Who's meeting whom?

Put matching hat stickers on the two animals whose sums have the same answer.

27-9

70-30

22-10

22-7

45-30

86-50

69-30

If you took away 10 from the sum on the monkey's suitcase,
what would the answer be? Write it here ....

Choosing ice cream

Do the sum on the label in the ice cream tub. Find the animal with the answer on its T-shirt and give it a cone sticker that matches the ice cream in the tub.

84
- 4

44
-22

62
-22

37
-12

40
- 3

15
- 8

18
- 4

29
-11

Ski race

Do the sum on the opposite page, then find a snowflake sticker with the answer and put it in the box.

Take away the number on the snake from the number on the panda.

Which number are you left with if you take 22 away from the number on the sheep?

If you take away 15 from the pig's number what would the answer be?

What is the difference between the panda and the sheep's numbers?

Which number do you get if you subtract 21 from the cat's number?

If you take 17 away from the snake's number, what would you be left with?

Take away the panda's number from the cat's, then subtract 7. What's the answer?

Quick thinking

Write the answers to these sums. Try to do them as quickly as you can. Use the pictures to help you, if you need to.

$7 - \boxed{} = 2$ $\boxed{} - 2 = 13$ $15 - 6 = \boxed{}$

$\boxed{} - 2 = 7$ $12 - 7 = \boxed{}$ $28 - \boxed{} = 4$

$9 - \boxed{} = 2$ $\boxed{} - 2 = 6$ $9 - 5 = \boxed{}$

Then, take away the crabs from the fish. Put a bird answer sticker on the roof.

$\square$ -12=7   28-7 = $\square$ 15- $\square$ =4

18- $\square$ =8 $\square$ -18=10   16-7 = $\square$

$\square$ -6=22   24-3 = $\square$ 18- $\square$ =6

At the fair

Which two bumper cars have sums with the same answer?
Do the sums, then, put the same animal sticker into the cars
with identical answers.

40
-20

27
-13

20
-11

34
- 4

18
- 9

70
-40

38
-24

46
-10

76
-40

32
-12

47

Climbing down ladders

Starting at the top, do the take-away sums, then put an answer sticker below the next rung on the ladder. Keep doing the sums until you reach the bottom of the ladders.

Ladder 1: 50, -3, [ ], -7, [ ], -6, [ ], -4, [ ]

Ladder 2: 40, -8, [ ], -2, [ ], -5, [ ], -5, [ ]

Ladder 3: 30, -5, [ ], -4, [ ], -3, [ ], -6, [ ]

Ladder with cat window: -8 area

For most pages, there are some extra stickers which are not answers to the sums.

page 26-27

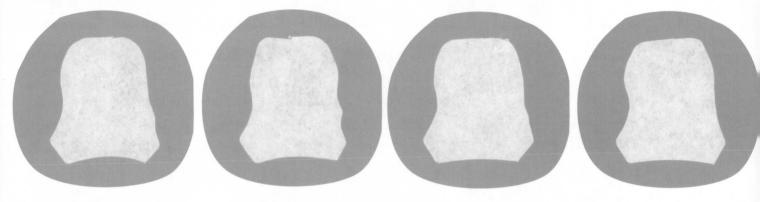

page 28-29

2	6	6	8	8	9	9	10	10	12
12	12	14	14	15	15	16	18	18	20
20	21	22	24	25	26	30	35	40	45

page 30-31

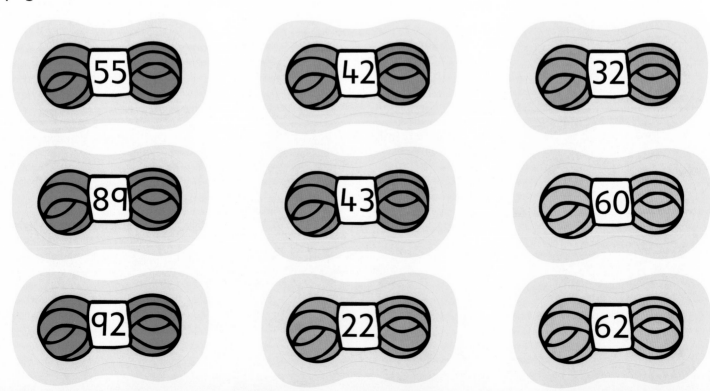

page 32-33

5 8 8 9 10 12 15 18

page 34-35

1 2 2 4 5 7 8

1 3 4 5 6 7 9

page 36

43 48 50 57 62 66 75 77

page 38-39

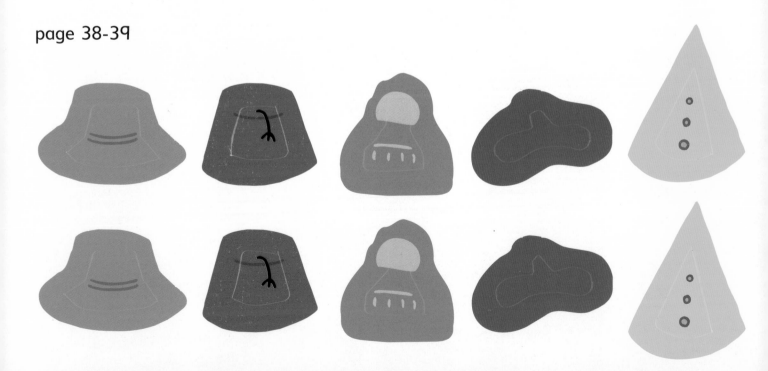

page 40-41

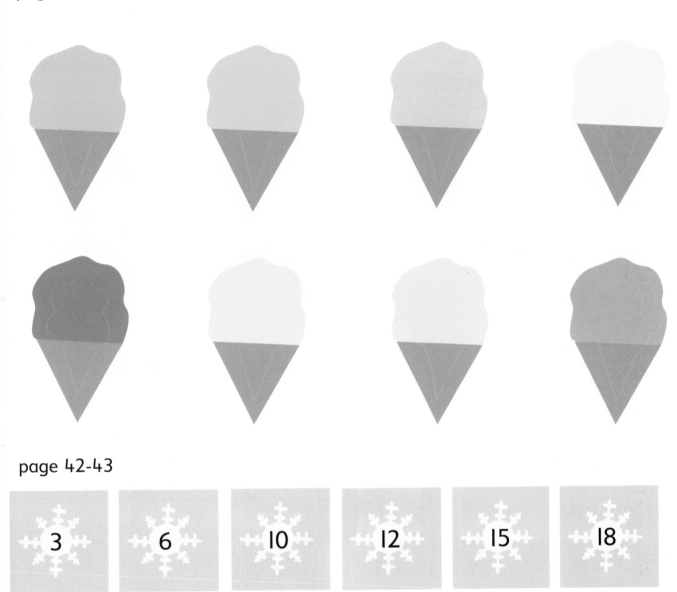

page 42-43

3	6	10	12	15	18
21	22	24	30	60	70

page 44-45

3 4 5 6

12	15	16	17	18	20	20	21
23	24	25	25	26	30	30	31
32	34	38	40	40	45	46	47

Times tables

Find the egg

Each baby bird is holding a times table sum. Do the sum, then find the egg sticker with the answer and put it in its nest.

5x2

3x2

8x2

51

Hands up

Each row of monkeys has a sum in a white box next to it. Put arm stickers on the monkeys so that the total number of fingers matches the answer.

4x5

6x5

Who's going on the plane?

Only the animals holding numbers which are in the five times table can get on the plane. Find stickers of them and put them into the windows on the plane.

54

What do numbers in the five times table end with? Write the answer .... or ....

Missing windows

Put window stickers into the spaces so that all the times table sums are correct.

5 x ⬜ = 50

⬜ x 10 = 70

3 x 10 = ⬜

⬜ x 10 = 20

8 x ⬜ = 80

☐ x 10 = 90

4 x 10 = ☐

☐ x 10 = 60

1 x 10 = ☐

☐ x 10 = 100

Where does Mole live?

Do the sum on the stone which is blocking Mole's path.
Draw an arrow along the tunnel which has the correct
answer, then do the sum on the next stone.
Continue doing this until you get to Mole's home.

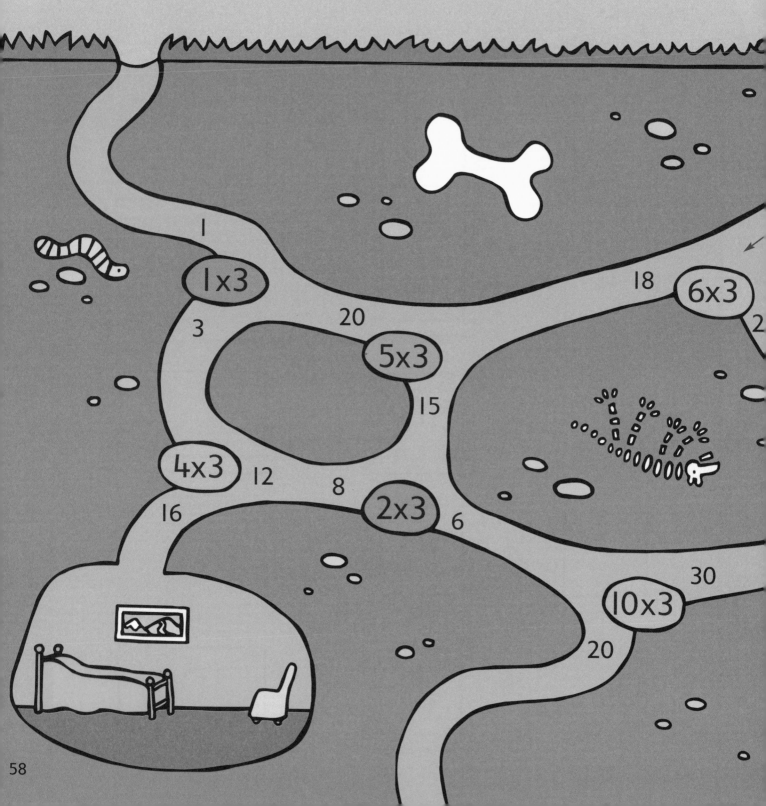

1

1x3

3

20

5x3

15

4x3   12

16   8

2x3   6

18   6x3

2

30

10x3

20

58

q

3x3

12

9x3

27

10

4x3

12

1

1x3

3

21

7x3

18

24

8x3

Put a sticker of a happy mole in his home.

21

59

Snails' shells

Multiply a number in the yellow circle by the number in the middle. Write the answer in the outside circle.

Double the number

Look at the number on an animal's cap and double it. Find the matching animal sticker with the answer and put it in the back seat of the car.

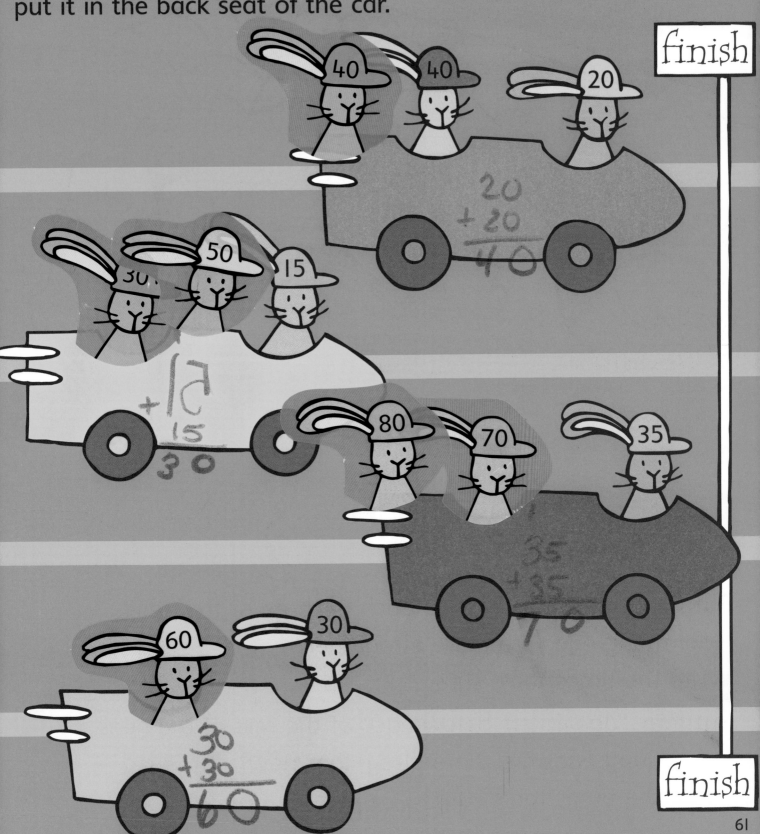

finish

finish

Hen house

Put four egg stickers below each of three of the hens.

How many eggs are there altogether? ☐

Write the times table sum ☐ x ☐ = ☐

Put four egg stickers below each of the rest of the hens.

How many eggs are there altogether now? ☐

Write the times table sum ☐ x ☐ = ☐

Put two spiders on each web.

How many spiders' legs are there altogether? ☐

Write the times table sum ☐ x ☐ = ☐

Put four mice running along the roof.

How many legs do the mice have altogether? ☐

Write the times table sum ☐ x ☐ = ☐

63

Washing line

Everything on the washing line has an adding sum on it. Put a butterfly sticker with the matching times table sum above each one.

5x7

7+7+7+7+7

8+8

7+7+7

6+6+6+6+6

Put a bug sticker on the sock
with the bigger answer.

6+6+6

8+8+8+8

7+7+7

8+8+8+8+8

Spiders' party

Find number stickers to finish the sums below.

How many legs does one spider have? 1 x 8 = ☐

How many legs do two spiders have altogether? 2 x 8 = ☐

Three spiders have ☐ legs altogether.

The times table sum for three spiders' legs is ☐ x ☐ = ☐

How many legs do four spiders have? ☐ x ☐ = ☐

Five spiders have ☐ legs altogether.

The times table sum for five spiders' legs is ☐ x ☐ = ☐

How many legs would 10 spiders have altogether? ☐

At the Bakery

Find out how many things are in each tray by counting the numbers of things in a row, then the number of rows. Multiply the two numbers together and put an answer sticker on the sign in the tray.

If you shared the bagels between 4 mice how many would each one get? Put the correct mouse sticker by the door.

Shark attack

Do the times table sum on each shark. Find the fish sticker with the answer and put it beside the shark's jaws.

Which shark is catching the fish with the biggest answer?
Put a sticker of a baby shark beside it.

Multiplication machine

Multiply the number on the first can by the number on the first machine. Put a can sticker with the answer on the conveyor belt. Then, multiply your answer by the number on the second machine and find its answer sticker, too.

For most pages, there are some extra stickers which are not answers to the sums.

page 50-51

2   4   5   6   8   10

12   14   16   18   20   22

page 52-53

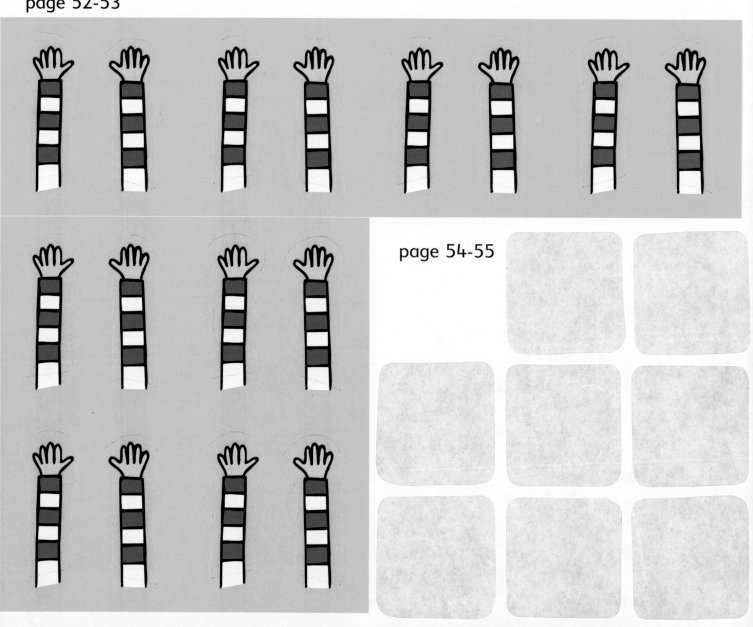

page 54-55

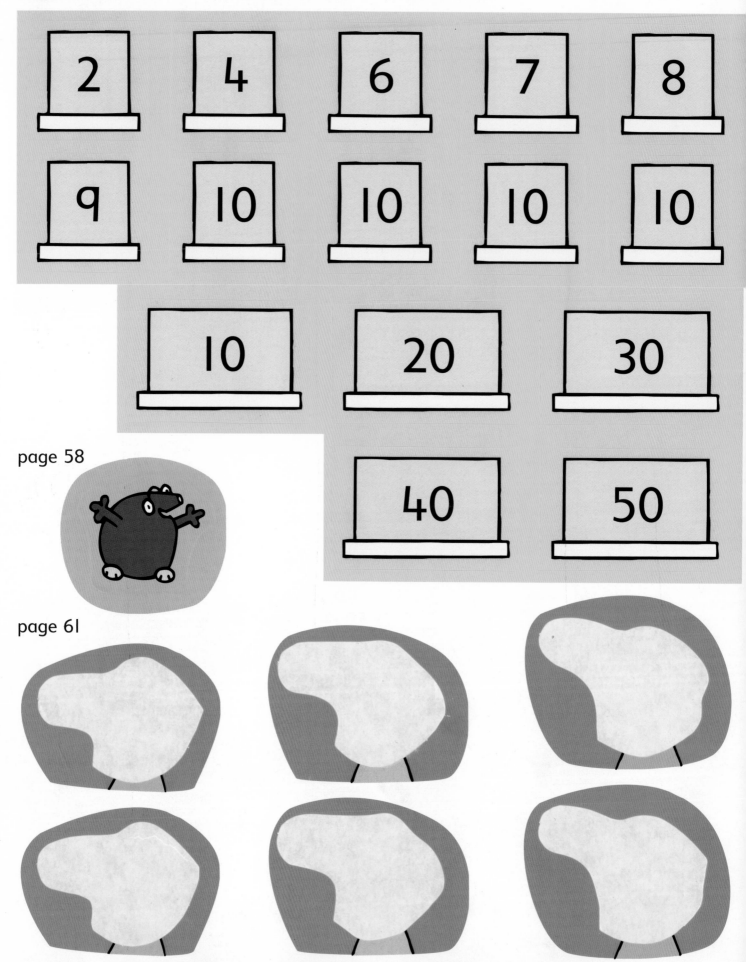

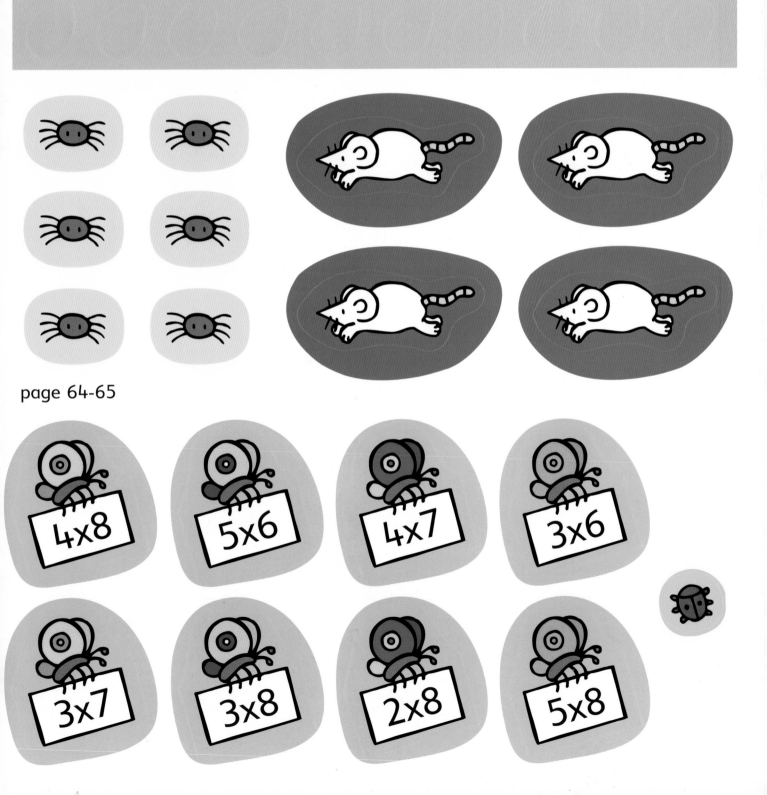

4x8 5x6 4x7 3x6

3x7 3x8 2x8 5x8

page 66-67

2 3 4 5 6 8 8 8 8 8 12 16 18 20 24

24 24 28 32 32 34 36 38 40 40 40 50 60 80 90

page 68-69

9 10 12 14

15 16 16 18

20 22 24 30

page 70-71

page 72

12 18 10 20 15 24

20 40 80 100 32 50

Fractions

Missing half

Make all the insects into whole insects by finding a matching sticker. Be careful to match the two halves exactly.

Cut in half?

Put a bee sticker beside all the food
which has been cut in half.

Halving shapes

Draw a line on each red shape on the robot's body so that they are divided in half. Try to divide similar shapes in different ways. You may not be able to.

Matching flowers

Put flower stickers onto the plants so that the flowers in the bottom half of the flower bed match the ones in the top half exactly.

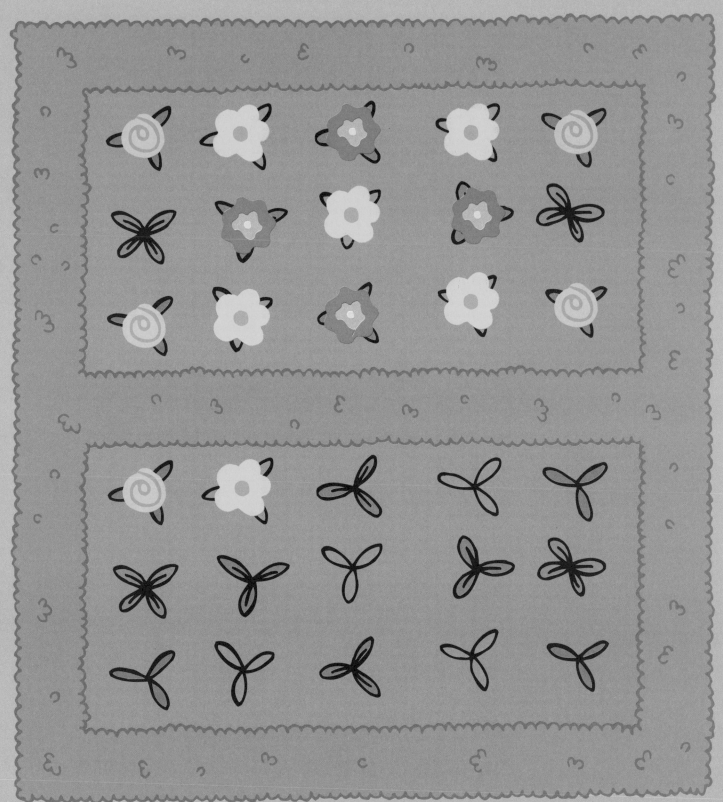

At the farm

Count the cows. Then, share the cow stickers between the two pens, putting half the total in each pen. Do the same for the other animals. Write the answers in the boxes.

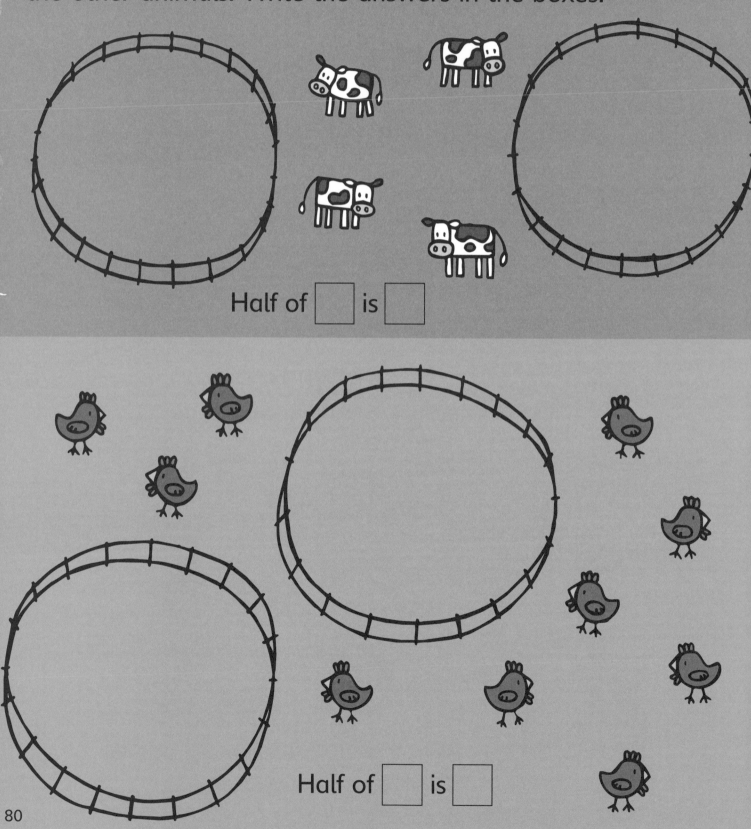

Half of ☐ is ☐

Half of ☐ is ☐

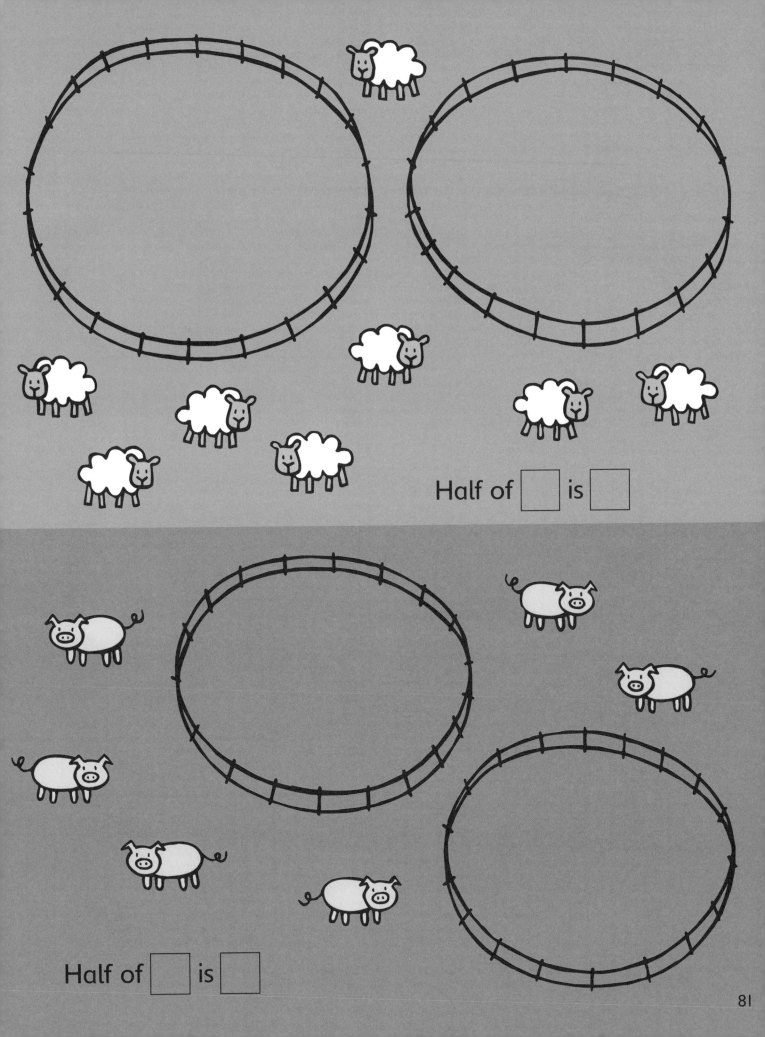

Half of ⬜ is ⬜

Half of ⬜ is ⬜

What's the time?

Write in the answers below the clocks
to show the correct time.

Half past **10**   Half past ⬚

Half past ⬚   Half past ⬚

Half past ⬚

Put the correct clock sticker on each clock to show the time written below it.

Half past 2

Half past 7

Half past 10

Half past 6

Half past 12

Half past 4

Turn around

If each rabbit did half a turn which way would it be facing?
Find the correct rabbit stickers.

Balancing numbers

The animals on one side of the see-saw are holding a whole number and the animals on the other side are each holding half the number. Find the correct number stickers so that the numbers balance.

On the fence

Find the bird stickers on the sticker pages, then put each one in the correct place on the fence.

9   10   11   12   13   14   15

2½

2   3   4   5   6   7   8

16   17   18   19   20   21   22

Space walk

Put a spacemouse sticker beside each shape which has been divided into quarters.

Something fishy

Draw a ring around one quarter of the fish in each group.
Fill in the boxes beside them.

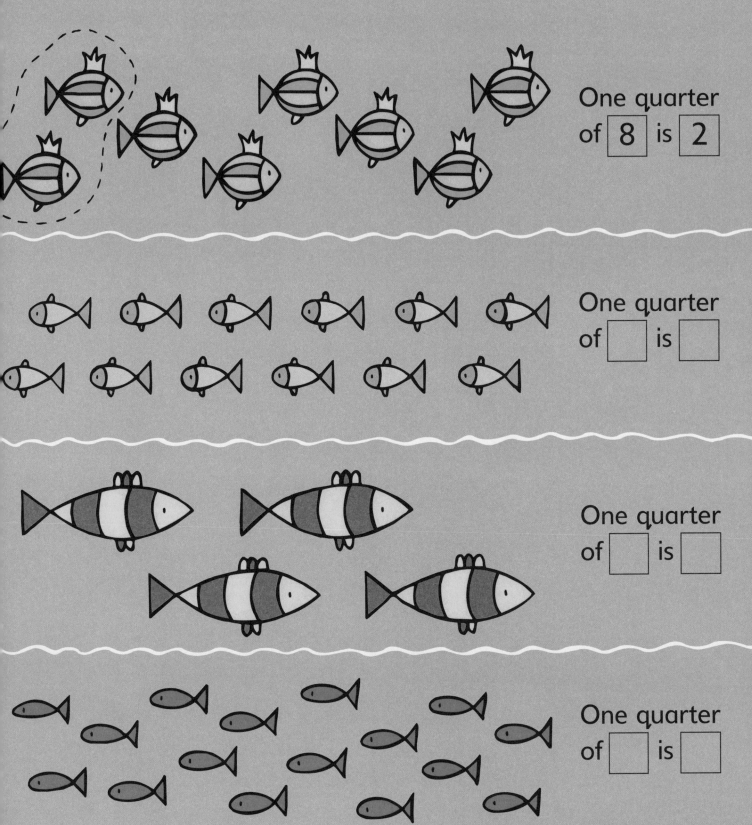

One quarter
of 8 is 2

One quarter
of ☐ is ☐

One quarter
of ☐ is ☐

One quarter
of ☐ is ☐

Watch out

Find the correct time sticker for each watch.

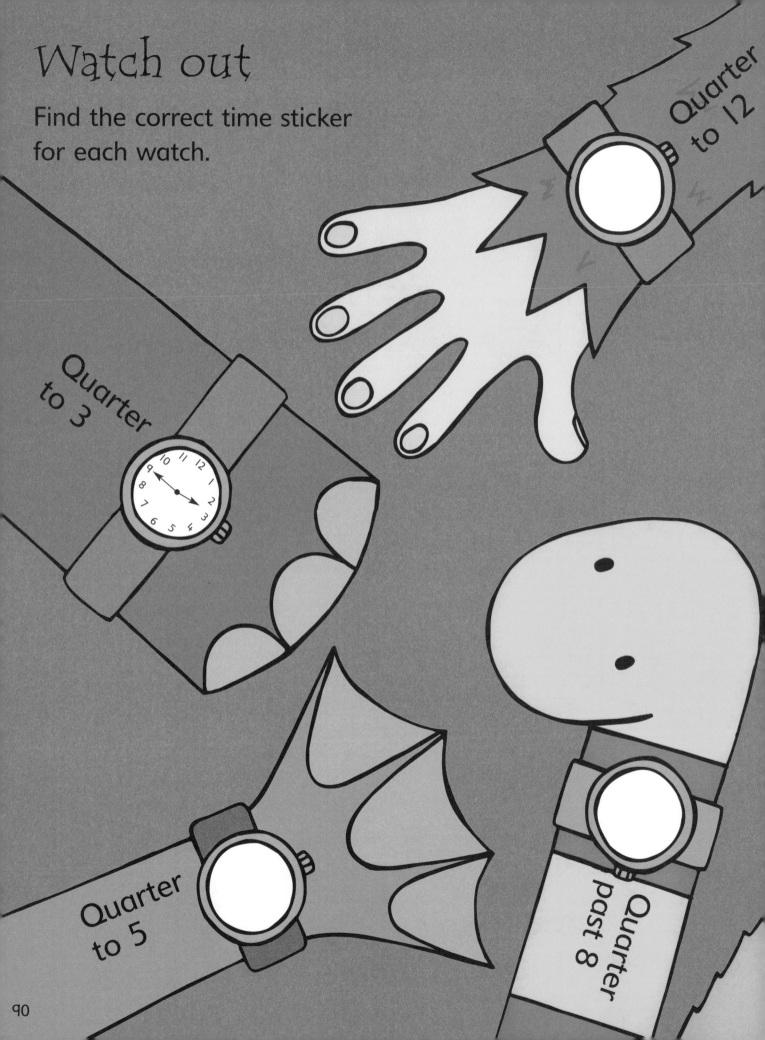

Quarter to 12

Quarter to 3

Quarter to 5

Quarter past 8

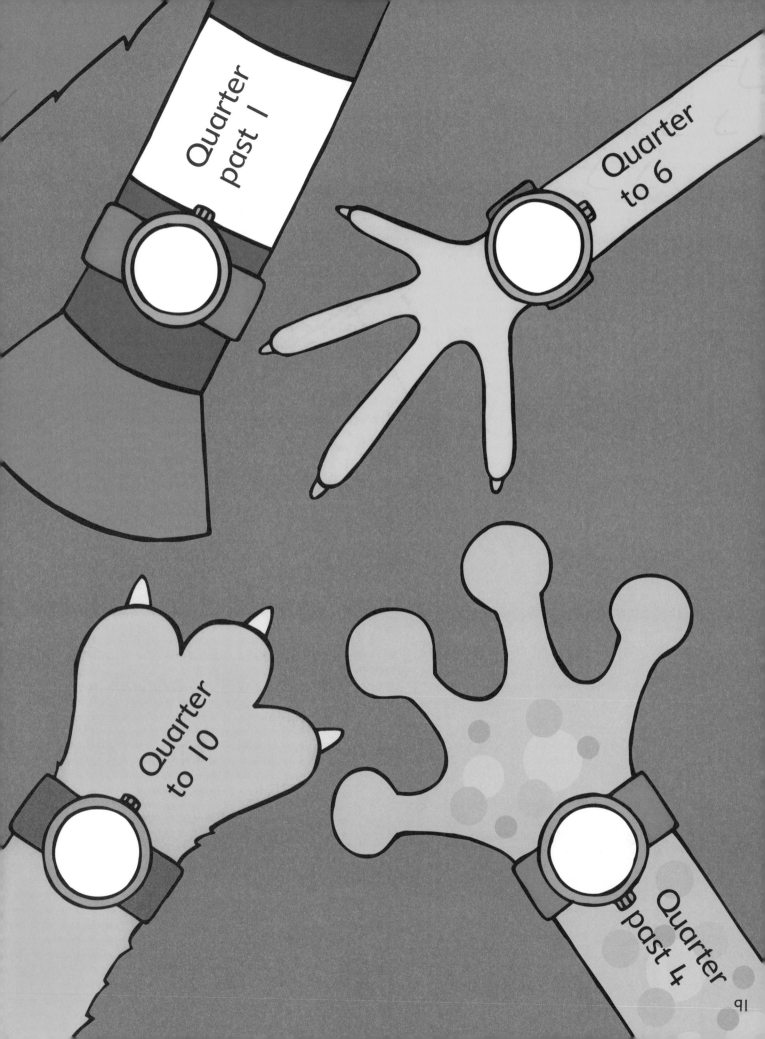

On the beach

Write in all the answers.

What fraction of the
shapes on the crabs'
flags is pink? ....

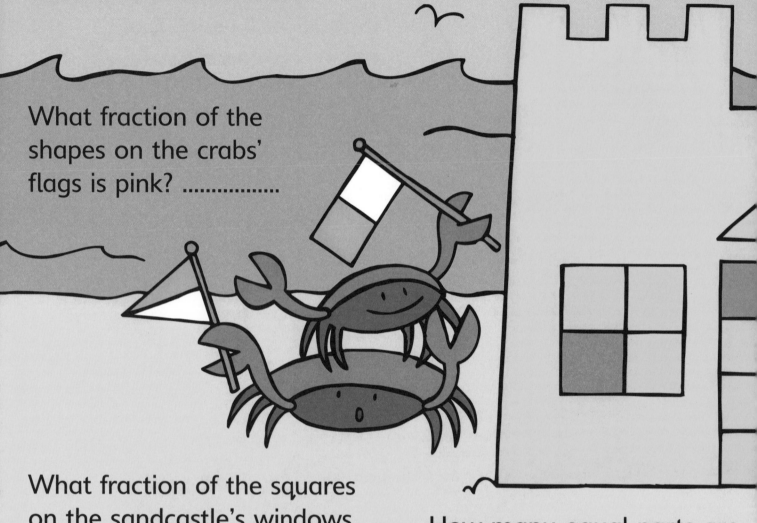

What fraction of the squares
on the sandcastle's windows
is blue? ....

How many equal parts are
there on the door of the
sandcastle? ....
What fraction of them is
green? ....

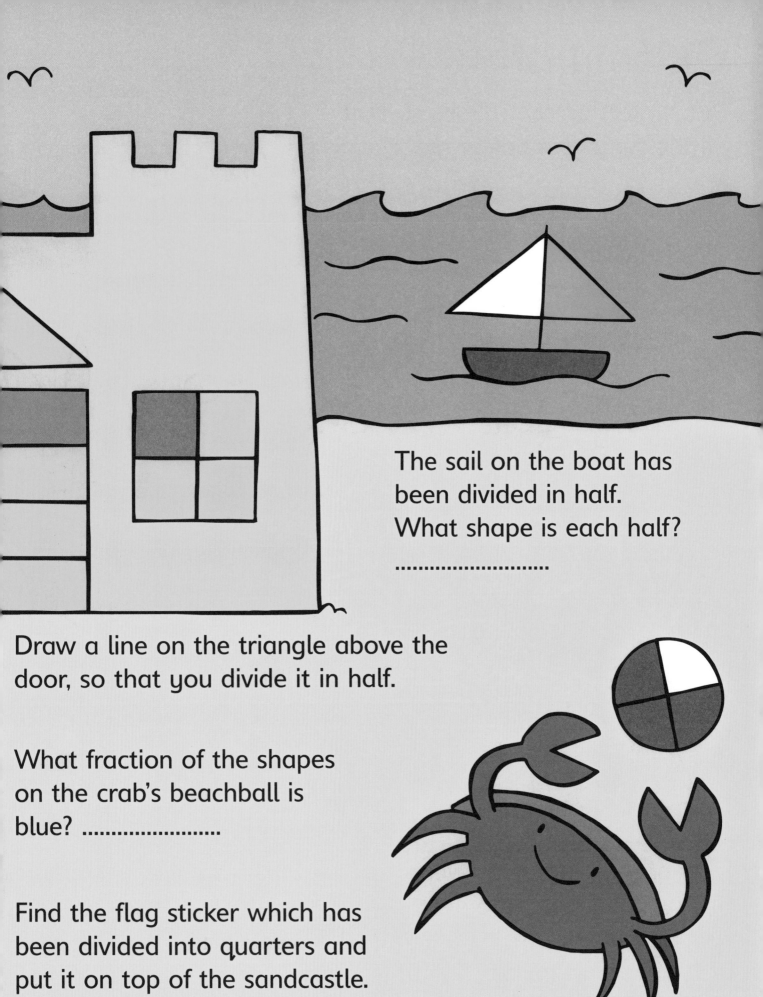

The sail on the boat has
been divided in half.
What shape is each half?

....

Draw a line on the triangle above the
door, so that you divide it in half.

What fraction of the shapes
on the crab's beachball is
blue? ....

Find the flag sticker which has
been divided into quarters and
put it on top of the sandcastle.

Getting dressed

Put stickers on the rabbits so that
all the sentences below are true.

Half of the rabbits are wearing striped boots and half
are wearing spotted ones.
¼ of the rabbits are wearing green sweatshirts.
The whole group is wearing hats.

A quarter of the rabbits are wearing gloves.
Three quarters of the rabbits are wearing red sweatshirts.
½ of the rabbits are wearing a scarf.

Pieces of chocolate

Fill in the boxes.

If the cat ate half the bar of chocolate, how many pieces
would he have eaten? ☐

If a ¼ of the bar of chocolate was shared between the mice,
how many pieces would each one get? ☐

If the mice shared the whole bar between them, what
fraction would each one get? ☐

If the cat ate a quarter of the bar, what fraction would be
left? ☐

For some of the pages, there are extra stickers which are not answers to the sums.

page 74-75

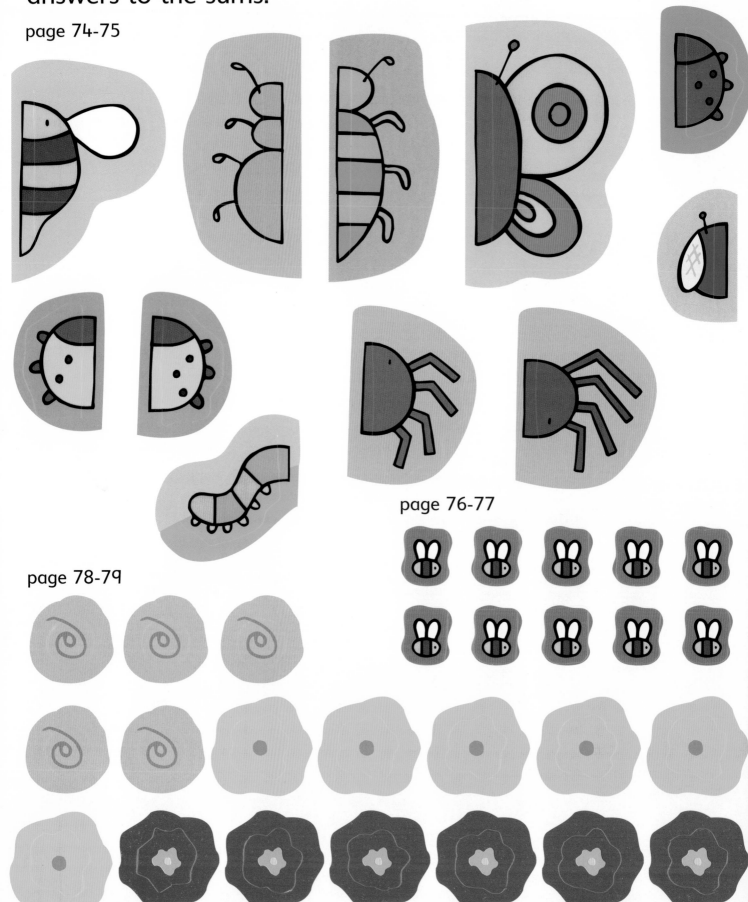

page 76-77

page 78-79

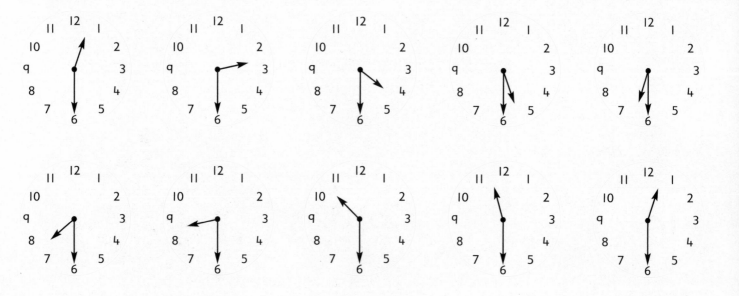

page 84

page 85

8 8 9 9 10 10 15 15 30 30 40 50

page 86-87

page 88

page 92-93

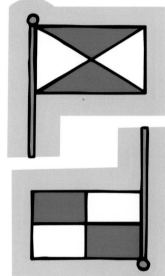

page 90-91

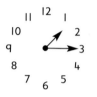  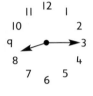

page 94-95

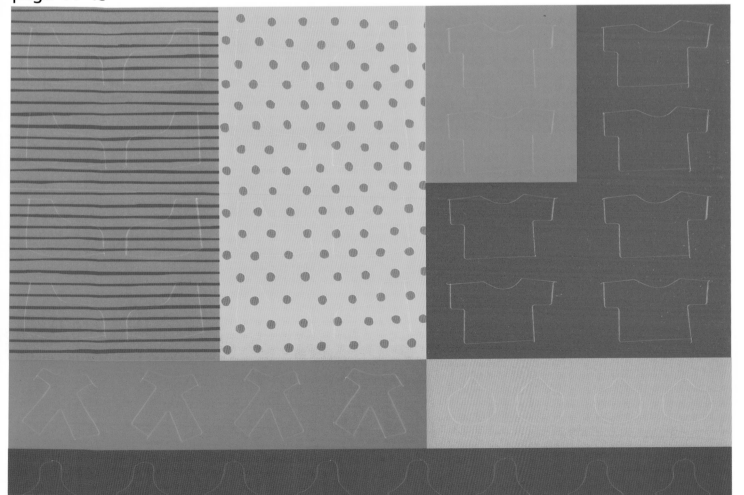